ONLINE ASSESSMENT POWERED BY PREP-U
THE ONLY TEST BANK & QUIZZING SYSTEM DEVELOPED BY THE TEXT AUTHOR IN NON-MAJORS BIOLOGY

The creation of Prep-U was spurred by Jay Phelan's frustration with traditional test banks. In response, he developed Prep-U, a multifaceted online assessment program. At its core are more than 4,000 class-tested and instructor-vetted multiple-choice questions of outstanding quality.

PREP-U FOR INSTRUCTORS TEST BANK

Exclusively for instructors using *What Is Life?*, this powerful Prep-U test bank offers the following for each chapter:

- ► 200 Practice Questions for homework or quizzing
- ► 75 Private Reserve Questions, hidden from student access, to be used in testing
- ► 5-10 Short-Answer Questions, with answers to help with grading
- ► 4 Essay Questions, also with suggested answers

Prep-U contains questions from all levels of the Bloom's Taxonomy scale, requiring students to know, understand, apply, analyze, synthesize, or evaluate. The system allows instructors to select, sequence, and modify existing questions and add their own favorites.

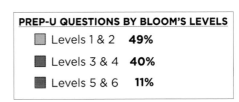

PREP-U QUESTIONS BY BLOOM'S LEVELS	
Levels 1 & 2	**49%**
Levels 3 & 4	**40%**
Levels 5 & 6	**11%**

Prep-U's data system offers a huge advantage to instructors. It enables them to evaluate how well each student is doing, how students compare with a national average, and which questions are posing difficulties.

In addition to including Bloom's Taxonomy level ratings, each Prep-U question includes a difficulty rating and a Misconception Index—a scale used to reveal common misunderstandings. Instructors can revisit those topics in class and even create Clicker questions to address them.

PREP-U FOR STUDENTS—FREE WITH ALL NEW COPIES OF WHAT IS LIFE?

Prep-U student quizzing is based on Personalized Adaptive Quizzing which compares student scores to nationwide results and then generates follow-up practice quizzes geared to the student's specific needs. Efficacy studies show that students who use Prep-U quizzing do better on tests than those who do not.

PREP-U FOR PHELAN'S *WHAT IS LIFE? A GUIDE TO BIOLOGY*
SAMPLE QUESTIONS

To allow you to judge the quality and of the questions in Prep-U, here is a sampling of 18 questions from the 285 questions offered for Chapter 8: Evolution and Natural Selection.

Each multiple-choice question has a textbook section reference, national percentages of right and wrong responses, a Difficulty Index, and a Bloom's Taxonomy level. Questions that reveal a significant level of student misunderstanding have a Misconception Index.

MULTIPLE-CHOICE QUESTIONS   * - Correct answer

Section 8.1: *We can see evolution occurring right before our eyes.*
Difficulty Index: 5 (of 100)   **Bloom's Level**: 1. Knowledge

Question: The average time to death from starvation in a fruit fly is about 20 hours. Selecting for increased starvation resistance in fruit flies:

Options	Results
a) can produce populations in which the average time to death from starvation is 10 hours through natural selection.	1%
b) has no effect because it is a not a trait that influences fruit fly fitness.	1%
c) has no effect because it is too complex a physiological process, dependent upon the effects of too many genes.	2%
d) can produce populations in which the average time to death from starvation is more than 160 hours because it is possible to change a population through natural selection.*	95%
e) has little effect because constant mutation reduces starvation resistance, counteracting any benefits from selection.	1%

Section 8.7: *Mutation—a direct change in the DNA of an individual—is the ultimate source of all genetic variation.*
Difficulty Index: 12 (of 100)   **Bloom's Level**: 3. Application

Question: Most mutations are:

Options	Results
a) beneficial or neutral to the organism in which the mutation takes place.	8%
b) random with respect to the environmental needs of the organism in which the mutation takes place.*	87%
c) found in regulator genes.	2%
d) found in the cytoplasm.	1%
e) accounted for by the Hardy-Weinberg equilibrium.	2%

Section 8.8: *Genetic drift is a random change in allele frequencies in a population change.*
Difficulty Index: 25 (of 100)   **Bloom's Level**: 2. Comprehension
Misconception Index: 35 (of 100)

Question: A power line cut has isolated 50 sowbugs from its original population of 15,000. After only five generations, the new population exhibits dramatic genetic differences from the original one, most likely because:

Options	Results
a) members of a small population tend to die off more quickly, removing alleles from the gene pool.	6%
b) gene flow increases in a new environment.	3%
c) the new environment is different from the old, favoring natural selection.	18%
d) mutations are more common near a power line.	4%
e) by chance, the allele frequencies of the isolated sowbugs differed from those in the original population, and subsequent genetic drift caused further divergence from the original gene pool.*	70%

Section 8.8: *Genetic drift is a random change in allele frequencies in a population change.*
Difficulty Index: 32 (of 100)   **Bloom's Level**: 2. Comprehension
Misconception Index: 33 (of 100)

Question: In a given population, a few individuals may, by random chance, leave behind more descendants than other individuals. Thus, the genes of the following generation will have a higher proportion of the alleles of the "lucky" individuals. Of which of the following concepts is this example representative?

Options	Results
a) genetic drift*	67%
b) migration	0%
c) mutation	7%
d) the founder effect	9%
e) the bottleneck effect	16%

Section 8.8: *Genetic drift is a random change in allele frequencies in a population change.*
Difficulty Index: 10 (of 100)   **Bloom's Level**: 1. Knowledge

Question: When a sudden change in the environment, such as a flood or fire, reduces the size of a population, the survivors' collective gene pool will be only a limited representation of what was present before the disaster. This phenomenon is called:

Options	Results
a) the bottleneck effect.*	6%
b) the founder effect.	3%
c) the Hardy-Weinberg effect.	18%
d) the culling effect.	4%
e) the genetic load.	70%

Section 8.10: *When three simple conditions are satisfied, evolution by natural selection is occurring.*
Difficulty Index: 45 (of 100)   **Bloom's Level**: 2. Comprehension
Misconception Index: 32 (of 100)

Question: The chief concern among conservation biologists trying to protect small populations is:

Options	Results
a) intraspecific competition.	11%
b) genetic diversity.*	57%
c) interspecific competition.	11%
d) predator density.	17%
e) runaway selection.	5%

Section 8.10: *When three simple conditions are satisfied, evolution by natural selection is occurring.*
Difficulty Index: 31 (of 100)   **Bloom's Level**: 4. Analysis
Misconception Index: 30 (of 100)

Question: Artificial selection was used on corn to produce a single strain of corn with increased growth rates and greater resistance to a fungus. Although farmers have continued to select for these traits, however, the productivity of this strain is no longer increasing. This suggests that:

Options	Results
a) the population size has been decreasing.	3%
b) artificial selection is not as strong as natural selection.	16%
c) gene migration is a major evolutionary agent in corn.	4%
d) all or most of the natural variation for these traits has been eliminated.*	66%
e) long term disruptive selection may lead to speciation.	11%

Section 8.10: *When three simple conditions are satisfied, evolution by natural selection is occurring.*
Difficulty Index: 31 (of 100)   **Bloom's Level**: 3. Application
Misconception Index: 35 (of 100)

Question: Many mosquito populations today are resistant to pesticides that were historically effective. This pesticide-resistance arose in these populations because:

Options	Results
a) the pesticides caused mutations in the DNA of mosquitoes that conferred resistance phenotypes, and were passed on to subsequent generations.	14%
b) populations had to develop tolerance in order to survive.	5%
c) individual mosquitoes build up immunity to the pesticides after exposure.	7%
d) some individuals were resistant to the pesticides before they were used, and those mosquitoes were more likely to survive and reproduce.*	75%
e) these populations were outside the range of the original pesticide application.	0%

Section 8.14: *Artificial selection is a special case of natural selection.*
Difficulty Index: 10 (of 100)   **Bloom's Level**: 3. Application

Question: Artificial selection is likely to produce population-level changes most quickly in organisms with:

Options	Results
a) a short generation time.*	88%
b) a large genome.	2%
c) a large genome.	2%
d) a long lifespan.	6%
e) a small litter size.	2%

Section 8.15: *Natural selection can change the traits in a population in several ways.*
Difficulty Index: 11 (of 100)   **Bloom's Level**: 2. Comprehension

Question: In a population of finches, birds with small, thick beaks can efficiently crack the seeds of one species of plant, while birds with long, thin beaks can efficiently crack the seeds of another plant species. Birds with medium-sized beaks cannot efficiently eat either kind of seed. After many generations, the distribution of beak size in these birds will be _____ because of _____.

Options	Results
a) bimodal; disruptive selection*	91%
b) normal; stabilizing selection	6%
c) skewed to the right; directional selection	3%
d) skewed to the left; directional selection	0%
e) linear; balancing selection	0%

Section 8.15: *Natural selection can change the traits in a population in several ways.*
Difficulty Index: 32 (of 100)   **Bloom's Level**: 4. Analysis
Misconception Index: 38

Question: Until the middle of the 19th century, all peppered moths (*Biston betularia*) observed around Manchester, England, were light in color. In 1845, a single black peppered moth was reported. As Manchester became more industrialized and dark soot began to cover the bark of the trees, the frequency of black moths increased greatly. The change in proportion of light and dark forms resulted from:

Options	Results
a) disruptive selection.	17%
b) directional selection.*	71%
c) stabilizing selection.	1%
d) sexual selection.	3%
e) increased mutation.	8%

Section 8.15: *Natural selection can change the traits in a population in several ways.*
Difficulty Index: 25 (of 100)   **Bloom's Level**: 4. Analysis
Misconception Index: 43 (of 100)

Question: In general, in a population in which a trait is exposed to stabilizing selection over time:

Options		Results
a)	the mean increases and variation decreases.	25%
b)	the mean increases and variation increases.	2%
c)	the mean becomes bimodal and the variation increases.	2%
d)	the mean stays approximately the same and the variation decreases.*	65%
e)	the mean stays approximately the same and the variation increases.	6%

Section 8.19: *Comparative anatomy and embryology reveal common evolutionary origins.*
Difficulty Index: 15 (of 100)   **Bloom's Level**: 3. Application

Question: Anatomical homology in vertebrate forelimbs is considered to be evidence for evolution because:

Options		Results
a)	similarities among vertebrate forelimbs suggest that they evolved from a common ancestor.*	86%
b)	differences among vertebrate forelimbs suggest that they evolved independently.	0%
c)	such homologies do not exist in other areas of the vertebrate skeleton.	0%
d)	similarities among vertebrate forelimbs suggest that they have evolved convergently.	12%
e)	the anatomy of the vertebrate forelimb is not currently under natural selection.	2%

1. Describe the relationship between mutation, evolution, and natural selection. Do these terms apply to individuals or populations?

Answer: Mutations are random changes in the DNA of individuals, and are the ultimate source of genetic variation. Through natural selection, individuals possessing beneficial variations are more likely to survive, and tend to produce more offspring than individuals lacking these beneficial mutations. Through this process, the population changes from one generation to the next and becomes better adapted to their environment. This change in the characteristics of the population is called evolution.

2. List the five primary lines of evidence that demonstrate the occurrence of evolution.

Answer: The five primary lines of evidence demonstrating the occurrence of evolution include the fossil record, biogeography, comparative anatomy and embryology, molecular biology, and laboratory and field experiments.

3. List the four agents of evolutionary change. Which of them make a population better adapted to its environment?

Answer: The four agents of evolutionary change are mutation, genetic drift, migration, and natural selection. Of these, only natural selection makes a population better adapted to its environment.

4. The evolutionary family tree for horses (see below) actually looks more like a bush than a tree. Explain why.

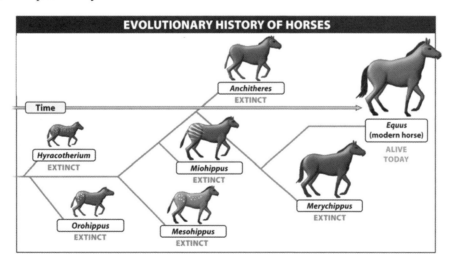

Answer: The modern horse that we know today is only a single branch of a "tree" that has had many other branches over the past 55 million years. Other branches of horses have split off over evolutionary time and flourished for millions of years before going extinct. While only *Equus* remains, it has not been the result of a simple linear path.

5. Why doesn't evolution produce "perfect" organisms? Is there a "perfect" beak size for a seed-eating Galá pagos finch?

Answer: Traits that are beneficial in the current environment tend to increase in frequency from one generation to the next. If the environment changes, these traits may no longer be beneficial and their frequencies may decrease. The "perfect" beak size in seed-eating Galá pagos finches is dependent uponseed availability – large in dry years when large, hard seeds must be eaten and smaller in wet years when small, soft seeds are more abundant. In short, there is no single "perfect" beak size.

6. In recent years, more and more frogs are appearing with mutated phenotypes. Propose an explanation for this observation.

Answer: Similar mutations have always occurred, but not at as high a rate as today. This increased mutation rate could be due to increased exposure to mutation-inducing chemicals or radiation found in today's more highly-polluted environments.

7. Why are most of the alleles fixed in present-day cheetah populations?

Answer: Modern-day cheetah populations descended from the very small number of cheetahs that survived a severe population bottleneck approximately 10,000 years ago. This small population lacked many of the alleles of previous populations, and even more alleles were lost through genetic drift over the next generations. Although there are a large number of cheetahs alive today, their genetic diversity is no greater than that of the bottleneck population.

faculty lounge
for non-majors biology

FACULTY LOUNGE FOR NON-MAJORS BIOLOGY
www.whfreeman.com/facultylounge/nonmajors

The first publisher-provided Web resource to link the Non-Majors Biology instructor community, the Faculty Lounge for Non-Majors Biology is the place to go for peer-provided, peer-reviewed lecture and teaching resources, as well as for Phelan instructor resource materials.

In the Faculty Lounge, instructors can view and download resources contributed by their colleagues nationwide—as well as contribute their own. Most importantly, they can communicate and share freely with colleagues nationwide who face the same challenges in the classroom.

The Faculty Lounge is continually updated and vetted by Non-Majors Biology instructors to ensure that there is always something new to see. Materials are categorized by topic and instructor-rated on a 5-star system for their usefulness in lectures or as sources of activities or projects. The site includes:

 VIDEOS AND ANIMATIONS suitable for starting off or enriching lectures

 SUPPLEMENTAL LECTURE IMAGES provide the best visual support for your lecture

 NEWS STORIES highlight the relevance of Biology in students' everyday lives

The Faculty Lounge is also a great source for Classroom Activity and Teaching Tips.

The complete set of Phelan **INSTRUCTOR RESOURCES** and **STUDENT RESOURCES** are also available for *What Is Life?* adopters to download through the Faculty Lounge.

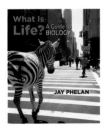

OVER ▶

faculty lounge
for non-majors biology

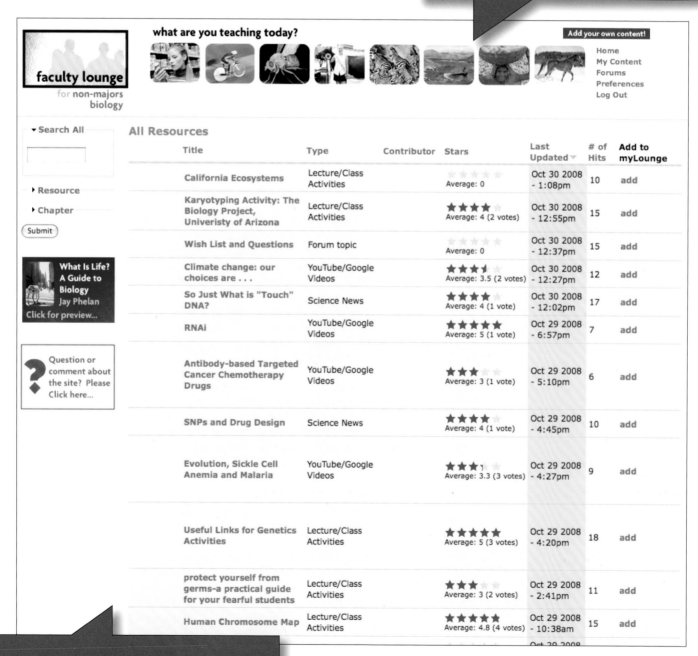

WHAT IS LIFE?

The eBook for *What Is Life?* offers everything from the text, all the student media, and a variety of personalized study tools found in a robust eBook environment. Instructors whose students are using the eBook can quickly and conveniently mark-up the e-text and add notes that only their students can view. To view a demo chapter of the eBook, go to **HTTP://EBOOKS.BFWPUB.COM**.

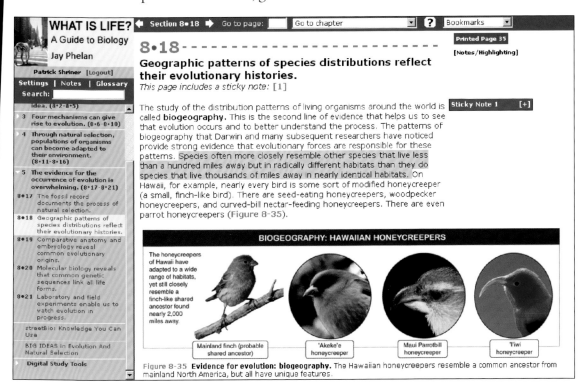

Figure 8-35 **Evidence for evolution: biogeography.** The Hawaiian honeycreepers resemble a common ancestor from mainland North America, but all have unique features.

eBook

INSTRUCTOR RESOURCES

The **INSTRUCTOR RESOURCES FOR PHELAN** are available to adopters for download through the **PHELAN FACULTY LOUNGE FOR NON-MAJORS BIOLOGY**. There is also an **INSTRUCTORS RESOURCE DVD** package available to adopters. Each tool has been carefully crafted to reflect the goals of *What Is Life?* as well as to bring the spirit of innovation evident in Prep-U and the Faculty Lounge.

IMAGE BANK, POWERPOINT PRESENTATIONS, & OVERHEAD TRANSPARENCIES

In recognition of the fact that most instructors' lectures are built around JPEG and PowerPoint files of images from the book, we have spent great time and care to ensure that these materials for *What Is Life?* are highly versatile and of the highest quality.

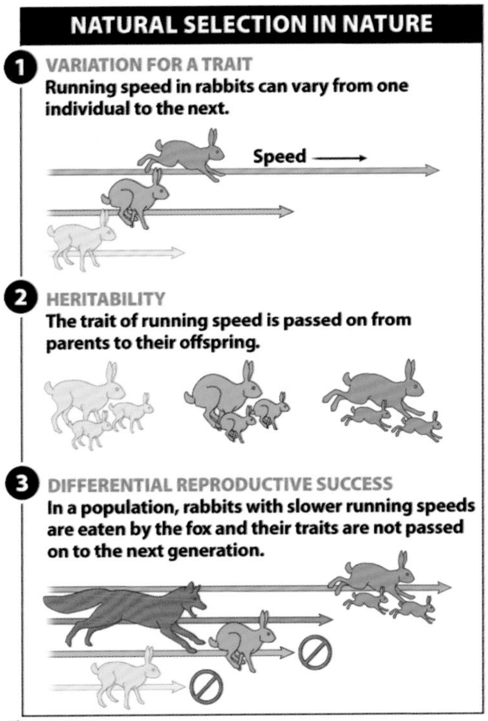

Our **IMAGE BANK** materials offer…
- ▶ All figures, photos, and tables from the book
- ▶ The stunning art program is fully optimized (including image-by-image attention to labels, lines, and colors)
- ▶ Each image was reviewed by instructors and projected in a large lecture hall to ensure visibility
- ▶ JPEG files in folders as well as JPEG files preloaded into PowerPoint
- ▶ All images available in labeled and unlabeled versions as well as with customizable labels
- ▶ Many complex figures rendered as step-by-step PowerPoint sequences
- ▶ **PHELAN'S FAVORITES**—striking author-supplied photos to augment text photos

NATURAL SELECTION IN NATURE

1 VARIATION FOR A TRAIT
Running speed in rabbits can vary from one individual to the next.

Speed ⟶

2 HERITABILITY
The trait of running speed is passed on from parents to their offspring.

3 DIFFERENTIAL REPRODUCTIVE SUCCESS
In a population, rabbits with slower running speeds are eaten by the fox and their traits are not passed on to the next generation.

Figure 8-20
What Is Life? A Guide to Biology
© 2010 W. H. Freeman and Company

POWERPOINT LECTURE OUTLINES include:
- ▶ Fully customizable presentations for each chapter of *What Is Life?*
- ▶ Slides featuring carefully edited content from the text and all figures, photos, and tables
- ▶ Lecture notes and figure captions for the instructor found in the "Notes" area of each slide, providing them with extra information without overwhelming the students
  Also offered in PowerPoint presentations for each chapter are…
- ▶ **ACTIVE LEARNING LECTURE OUTLINES**—incorporating Clicker Questions, classroom activities, and Phelan **Q** Animations

KEYNOTE presentations for each chapter are available for Macintosh users.

OVERHEAD TRANSPARENCY SET
- ▶ Every figure from the text with labels enhanced for clear visibility in large lecture halls

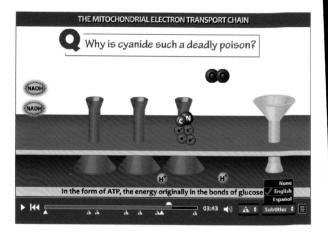

PHELAN Q ANIMATIONS IN POWERPOINT

Based on the art from the text, these animations bring to life some of the most challenging topics to visualize.

- ▶ Topics include: Chemistry, the Cell, Photosynthesis, Cellular Respiration, Transcription, Translation, DNA, Mitosis, Meiosis, Genetics, and Evolution
- ▶ Following the lead of the book, most of the core animated topics are preceded by a "Big Picture" animation that offers a broader overview and stresses the relevancy of the core concept to students' lives
- ▶ Biological relevancy is also reinforced by offering each animation in the context of an engaging **Q** question from the text
- ▶ All animations have voiceovers and onscreen subtitles in English and Spanish; voiceovers and subtitles can be easily turned on and off
- ▶ The animation files are preloaded into PowerPoint files to save time

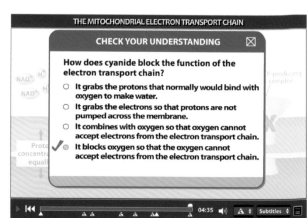

INSTRUCTOR'S MANUAL

The **INSTRUCTOR'S MANUAL** helps both new and experienced instructors tie together all *What Is Life?* media and supplements…

- ▶ **CHAPTER OUTLINES**, **KEY TERMS**, and **LEARNING OBJECTIVES** show instructors chapter coverage at a glance
- ▶ **CLASSROOM CATALYSTS** engage students with discussion questions and active learning techniques incorporating **Q** questions and working off common student misconceptions; designed for classrooms of any size or budget, 10–30 minutes each
- ▶ **STUDENT WORKSHEETS** suitable for handing out before lecture require students to analyze and answer questions about the most important figures from each chapter; especially helpful for visual learners
- ▶ **ECO-FRIENDLY!** The instructor's manual is available online or on CD/DVD; print copies will be available upon request

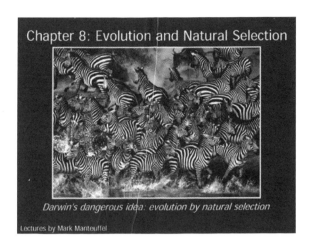

Chapter 8: Evolution and Natural Selection

Darwin's dangerous idea: evolution by natural selection

Lectures by Mark Manteuffel

Learning Objectives

❑ Be able to explain evolution in action.

❑ Be able to explain Darwin's journey to an idea.

❑ Be able to describe and explain the four mechanisms that can give rise to evolution.

Learning Objectives

❑ Be able to explain how populations of organisms can adapt to their environment through natural selection.

❑ Be able to explain how the evidence for the occurrence of evolution is overwhelming.

What is your opinion? The human population on our planet is evolving.

1. Yes
2. No
3. Unsure

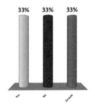

33%   33%   33%

Evolution in Action

8-1. We can see evolution occur right before us.

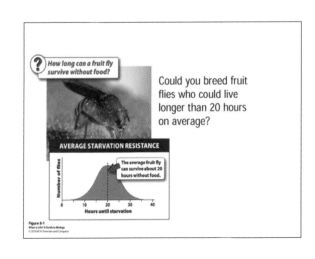

? How long can a fruit fly survive without food?

Could you breed fruit flies who could live longer than 20 hours on average?

AVERAGE STARVATION RESISTANCE

The average fruit fly can survive about 20 hours without food.

Number of flies

Hours until starvation

Figure 8-1
What is Life? A Guide to Biology
© 2010 W.H. Freeman and Company

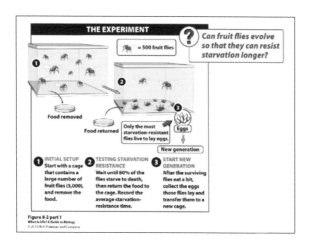

Figure 8-2 part 1
What Is Life? A Guide to Biology
© 2010 W. H. Freeman and Company

THE EXPERIMENT

= 500 fruit flies

Can fruit flies evolve so that they can resist starvation longer?

Food removed

Food returned

Only the most starvation-resistant flies live to lay eggs.

Eggs

New generation

1 INITIAL SETUP Start with a cage that contains a large number of fruit flies (5,000), and remove the food.

2 TESTING STARVATION RESISTANCE Wait until 80% of the flies starve to death, then return the food to the cage. Record the average starvation-resistance time.

3 START NEW GENERATION After the surviving flies eat a bit, collect the eggs those flies lay and transfer them to a new cage.

When these eggs hatch, do you think the flies in this new generation will live longer than 20 hours without food?

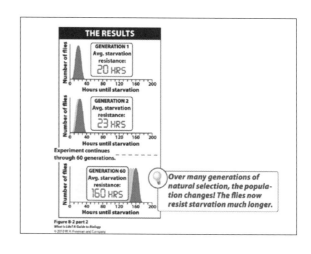

? How long can a fruit fly survive without food?

AVERAGE STARVATION RESISTANCE

The average fruit fly can survive about 20 hours without food.

Number of flies

Hours until starvation

Figure 8-1
What Is Life? A Guide to Biology
© 2010 W. H. Freeman and Company

Make a prediction: A population of fruit flies was starved until 80% of the flies were dead. The remaining flies were fed and offspring were produced. What do you expect to see in the next generation if you repeat the starvation experiment?

1. More flies will be alive after 20 hours.
2. Fewer flies will be alive after 20 hours.
3. Fruit flies fed after 80% of the population is dead will lay more eggs.
4. No change in the average number of fruit flies that were alive after 20 hours.

25% 25% 25% 25%

More flies will... / Fewer flies will... / Fruit flies fe... / No change in t...

THE RESULTS

GENERATION 1
Avg. starvation resistance:
20 HRS
Hours until starvation

GENERATION 2
Avg. starvation resistance:
23 HRS
Hours until starvation

Experiment continues through 60 generations.

GENERATION 60
Avg. starvation resistance:
160 HRS
Hours until starvation

Over many generations of natural selection, the population changes! The flies now resist starvation much longer.

Figure 8-2 part 2
What Is Life? A Guide to Biology
© 2010 W. H. Freeman and Company

After 60 generations the average starvation resistance of fruit flies was **160 hours!** What has happened to this population of fruit flies?

1. They are genetically identical to the original population.

2. The are genetically different from the original population.

50%   50%

They are genet... / They are genet...

What happened?

❑ **Evolution**
  • a genetic change in the population

❑ **Natural selection**
  • certain individuals are born with characteristics that enable them to survive better and reproduce more than other individuals

Does evolution occur?

❑ The answer is an unambiguous: **YES**.

❑ We can watch it happen in the lab whenever we want.

Experiments in Evolution

❑ Dogs?

❑ Rabbits?

Evolution

❑ How does evolution occur?

❑ What types of changes can evolution cause in a population?

❑ Five primary lines of evidence

❑ Evolution by natural selection

Take-home message 8-1

❑ The characteristics of individuals in a population can change over time.

❑ We can observe such change in nature and can even cause such change to occur.

8-8. Genetic drift is a random change in allele frequencies in a population.

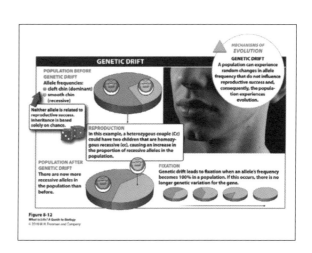

The important factor that distinguishes genetic drift from natural selection:

*The change in allele frequencies is **not** related to the alleles' influence on reproductive success.*

The impact of genetic drift is much greater in small populations than in large populations.

Fixation

- Genetic drift can lead to **fixation** for one allele for a gene in a population.

- If this happens, there is no more variability in the population for this gene.

- **Genetic drift reduces the genetic variation in a population.**

Two special cases of genetic drift, the **founder effect** and **population bottlenecks**, are important in the evolution of populations.

Founder Effect

- A small number of individuals may leave a population and become the founding members of a new, isolated population.

- The founders may have different allele frequencies than the original "source" population, particularly if they are a small sample.

Why are Amish people more likely to have extra fingers and toes?

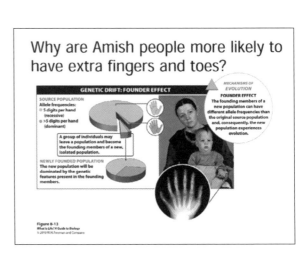

Population Bottlenecks

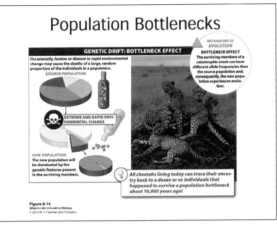

Genetic Drift: Part A

1. Each student in the front row gets 3 red and 3 black cards.

2. Each student in the front row picks a card (allele) from their deck (population).

3. Record observations.

4. Pass the cards to students in the second row and repeat.

5. Pass the cards to students in the third row and repeat.

What affected whether you picked a red or black card from your pile containing 3 red and 3 black cards?

1. Natural selection
2. Random chance
3. There was a higher probability of picking red cards.
4. There was a higher probability of picking black cards.

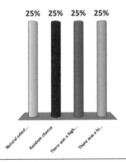

Genetic Drift: Part B

Let's assume that one of the trials from our first experiment yields a larger proportion of red cards than black cards. How will this affect genetic drift?

1. Each student in the front row gets 4 red cards and 2 black cards.
2. Repeat the experiment as before and record your results.

Which scenario would delay or possibly prevent the fixation of the red card (allele) in the deck (population)?

1. Fixation will happen no matter what.
2. Use a larger deck (population).
3. Use more colors (alleles) of cards but start with a total of 6 cards.
4. All of the above.

Take-home message 8-8

❑ Genetic drift is a random change in allele frequencies within a population, unrelated to the alleles' influence on reproductive success.

❑ Genetic drift is a significant agent of evolutionary change primarily in small populations.

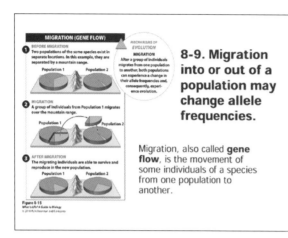

8-9. Migration into or out of a population may change allele frequencies.

Migration, also called **gene flow**, is the movement of some individuals of a species from one population to another.

Take-home message 8-9

❑ Migration, or gene flow, leads to a change in allele frequencies in a population as individuals move into or out of the population.

8-10. When three simple conditions are satisfied, evolution by natural selection occurs.

1. There must be variation for the particular trait within a population.

2. That variation must be inheritable.

3. Individuals with one version of the trait must produce more offspring than those with a different version of the trait.

Condition 1: Variation for a Trait

❑ Variation is all around us.
❑ Variation is the raw material on which evolution feeds.

Condition 2: Heritability

We call the transmission of traits from parents to their children through genetic information **inheritance** or **heritability**.

Condition 3: Differential Reproductive Success

1. There are more organisms born than can survive.

Condition 3: Differential Reproductive Success

2. Organisms are continually struggling for existence.

Condition 3: Differential Reproductive Success

3. Some organisms are more likely to win this struggle and survive and reproduce.

Differential Reproductive Success

Individuals with traits most suited to reproduction generally leave more offspring than individuals with other traits.

The tiniest dog in a litter has reduced differential reproductive success. Its more robust siblings prevent access to the food it needs to grow and thrive.

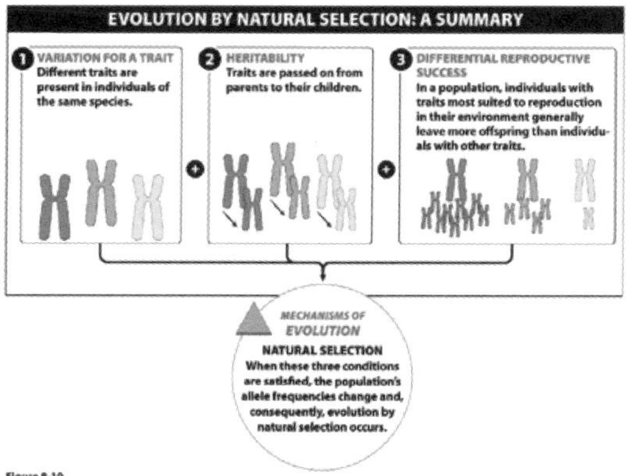

Figure 8-18
What is Life? A Guide to Biology
© 2010 W. H. Freeman and Company

EVOLUTION BY NATURAL SELECTION: A SUMMARY

1 **VARIATION FOR A TRAIT**
Different traits are present in individuals of the same species.

2 **HERITABILITY**
Traits are passed on from parents to their children.

3 **DIFFERENTIAL REPRODUCTIVE SUCCESS**
In a population, individuals with traits most suited to reproduction in their environment generally leave more offspring than individuals with other traits.

MECHANISMS OF EVOLUTION

NATURAL SELECTION
When these three conditions are satisfied, the population's allele frequencies change and, consequently, evolution by natural selection occurs.

Figure 8-19
What Is Life? A Guide to Biology
© 2010 W. H. Freeman and Company

Most agricultural pests evolve resistance to pesticides.

How does this happen?

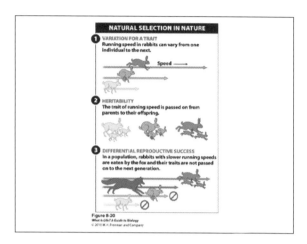

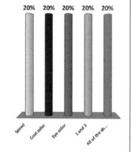

Which trait in rabbits (listed below) has evolved due to interactions with predators?

1. Speed
2. Coat color
3. Eye color
4. 1 and 2
5. All of the above

Take-home message 8-10

❑ Natural selection occurs when there is heritable variation for a trait, and individuals with one version of the trait have greater reproductive success than individuals with a different version of the trait.

Figure 8-16 part 1
What Is Life? A Guide to Biology
© 2010 W. H. Freeman and Company

Figure 8-16 (part 1) Necessary conditions for natural selection: 1. Variation for a trait.

- Close your eyes and imagine a dog. What does the dog look like?
- Chances are, if 50 people were asked this question, we would get descriptions of 50 different dogs (Fig. 8-16).
- Chihuahuas, Great Danes, sheep dogs, greyhounds, spaniels, and more. Some are big, some are small. Some have short hair, some long.
- They vary in just about every way that you can imagine.

Condition 1: Variation for a Trait

❑ Variation is all around us.

❑ Variation is the raw material on which evolution feeds.

Figure 8-16 part 2
What is Life? A Guide to Biology
© 2010 W. H. Freeman and Company

- Similarly, if 50 people were to imagine a human face, a similarly broad range of images would pop into their heads.
- Variation is all around us.
- Beyond making the world an interesting place to live, variation serves another purpose: it is the raw material on which evolution feeds.
- Variation is not limited to physical features such as fur color and texture or face shape and eye color.
- Organisms vary in physiological and biochemical ways, too.
- Some people can quickly and efficiently metabolize alcohol, for example. Others find themselves violently ill soon after sipping a glass of wine. The same goes for digesting milk. Similarly, we vary in our susceptibility to poison ivy or diseases such as malaria.
- Behavioral variation—from temperament to learning abilities to interpersonal skills—is dramatic and widespread, too.
- So impressed was Darwin with the variation he observed throughout the world, he devoted the first two chapters of The Origin of Species to a discussion of variation in nature and among domesticated animals.
- Darwin knew that the variation he saw all around him was an essential component to evolution by natural selection.
- He considered it the first of three conditions necessary for natural selection.

Condition 2: Heritability

We call the transmission of traits from parents to their children through genetic information **inheritance** or **heritability**.

Figure 8-17
What is Life? A Guide to Biology
© 2012 W.H.Freeman and Company

- The second of the conditions that Darwin identified as necessary for natural selection was no more of a complex discovery than the first.
- It was that for natural selection to act on a trait within a population, offspring must inherit the trait from their parents.
- Although inheritance was poorly understood in Darwin's time, it was not hard to see that for many traits offspring look more like their parents than they do some other random individual in the population (Fig. 8-17).
- Animal breeders had long known that the fastest horses generally gave birth to the fastest horses.
- Farmers, too, understood that the plants with the highest productivity generally produced seeds from which highly productive plants grew.
- And everyone knew that children resembled their parents, from their appearance to their behavior to their temperament.
- It was enough to know that this similarity between offspring and parents existed—it was not necessary to understand how it occurred or to be able to quantify just how great the similarity was.
- We call the transmission of traits from parents to their children through genetic information inheritance or heritability.

Chapter 8
Evolution and Natural Selection

Learning Objectives

- Understand how evolution can be observed in various populations.
- Describe Charles Darwin's impact on evolution and the study of biology.
- Identify the individuals who influenced Darwin.
- Describe Darwin's most important observations.
- Explain the four ways evolutionary change can take place.
- Identify the difference between evolution and natural selection.
- Understand and explain the five different lines of evidence for the occurrence of evolution.
- Describe ways evolution can be observed today.

Chapter Outline

1   Evolution is an ongoing process.

8.1 We can see evolution occurring right before our eyes.
TAKE-HOME MESSAGE 8-1: The characteristics of individuals in a population can change over time. We can observe such change in nature and can even cause such change to occur.

2   Darwin's journey to a new idea.

8.2 Before Darwin, most people believed that all species had been created separately and were unchanging.
TAKE-HOME MESSAGE 8-2: In the eighteenth and nineteenth centuries, scientists began to overturn the commonly held beliefs that the earth was only about 6,000 years old and that all species had been created separately and were unchanging. These gradual changes in scientists' beliefs helped shape Charles Darwin's thinking.

8.3 A job on a 'round-the-world survey ship allowed Darwin to indulge and advance his love of nature.
TAKE-HOME MESSAGE 8-3: After initially training in medicine and theology, Charles Darwin was able to focus on studying the natural world when, in 1831, he got a job on a ship conducting a five-year, 'round-the-world survey.

8.4 Observing geographic similarities and differences among fossils and living plants and animals, Darwin developed a theory of evolution.
TAKE-HOME MESSAGE 8-4: Darwin noted unexpected patterns among fossils he found and living organisms he observed while on the voyage of the *Beagle*. Fossils resembled but were not identical to the living organisms in the same area in which they were found. And finch species on each of the Galápagos Islands differed from each other

in small but significant ways. These observations helped Darwin to develop his theory of how species might change over time.

8.5 In 1858, Darwin published his thoughts on natural selection after decades of percolating and procrastinating.
TAKE-HOME MESSAGE 8-5: After putting off publishing his thoughts on natural selection for more than 15 years, Darwin did so only after Alfred Russel Wallace independently came up with the same idea. The two men published a joint presentation on their ideas in 1858, and Darwin published a much more detailed treatment in *The Origin of Species* in 1859, sparking wide debate and discussion of natural selection.

3   Four mechanisms can give rise to evolution.

8.6 Evolution occurs when the allele frequencies in a population change.
TAKE-HOME MESSAGE 8-6: Evolution is a change in allele frequencies within a population. It can occur by four different mechanisms: mutation, genetic drift, migration, and natural selection.

8.7 Mutation—a direct change in the DNA of an individual—is the ultimate source of all genetic variation.
TAKE-HOME MESSAGE 8-7: Mutation is an alteration of the base-pair sequence in an individual's DNA. Such an alteration constitutes evolution if it changes an allele that the individual carries. Mutations can be caused by high-energy sources or chemicals in the environment and also can appear spontaneously. Mutation is the only way that new alleles can be created within a population, and so generates the variation on which natural selection can act.

8.8 Genetic drift is a random change in allele frequencies in a population.
TAKE-HOME MESSAGE 8-8: Genetic drift is a random change in allele frequencies within a population, unrelated to the alleles' influence on reproductive success. Genetic drift is a significant agent of evolutionary change primarily in small populations.

8.9 Migration into or out of a population may change allele frequencies.
TAKE-HOME MESSAGE 8-9: Migration, or gene flow, leads to a change in allele frequencies in a population as individuals move into or out of the population.

8.10 When three simple conditions are satisfied, evolution by natural selection is occurring.
TAKE-HOME MESSAGE 8-10: Natural selection is a mechanism of evolution that occurs when there is heritable variation for a trait and individuals with one version of the trait have greater reproductive success than do individuals with a different version of the trait. It can also be thought of as the elimination of alleles from a population that reduce the reproductive rate of individuals carrying those alleles relative to the reproductive rate of individuals who do not carry the alleles.

4   Through natural selection, populations of organisms can become adapted to their environment.

8.11 Traits causing some individuals to have more offspring than others become more prevalent in the population.

TAKE-HOME MESSAGE 8-11: Fitness is a measure of the relative amount of reproduction of an individual with a particular phenotype, as compared with the reproductive output of individuals with alternative phenotypes. An individual's fitness can vary, depending on the environment in which the individual lives.

8.12 Organisms in a population can become better matched to their environment through natural selection.
TAKE-HOME MESSAGE 8-12: Adaptation—the process by which organisms become better matched to their environment and the specific features that make an organism more fit—occurs as a result of natural selection.

8.13 Natural selection does not lead to perfect organisms.
TAKE-HOME MESSAGE 8-13: Natural selection does not lead to organisms perfectly adapted to their environment because (1) environments can change more quickly than natural selection can adapt organisms to them; (2) all possible alleles are not produced by mutation; (3) there is not always a single optimum adaptation for a given environment.

8.14 Artificial selection is a special case of natural selection.
TAKE-HOME MESSAGE 8-14: Animal breeders and farmers utilize natural selection when they modify their animals and crops because the three conditions for natural selection are satisfied. Because the differential reproductive success is determined by humans and not by nature, this type of natural selection is also called artificial selection.

8.15 Natural selection can change the traits seen in a population in several ways.
TAKE-HOME MESSAGE 8-15: Acting on multigene traits for which populations show a large range of phenotypes, natural selection can change populations in several ways, including (1) directional selection, in which the average value for the trait increases or decreases; (2) stabilizing selection, in which the average value of a trait remains the same while extreme versions of the trait are selected against; and (3) disruptive selection, in which individuals with extreme phenotypes have the highest fitness.

8.16 Natural selection can cause the evolution of complex traits and behaviors.
TAKE-HOME MESSAGE 8-16: Natural selection can change allele frequencies for genes involving complex physiological processes and behaviors. Sometimes a trait that has been selected for one function is later modified to serve a completely different function.

5 The evidence for the occurrence of evolution is overwhelming.

8.17 The fossil record documents the process of natural selection.
TAKE-HOME MESSAGE 8-17: Radiometric dating confirms that the earth is very old and makes it possible to determine the age of fossils. Analysis of fossil remains enables biologists to reconstruct what organisms looked like long ago, learn how organisms were related to each other, and understand how groups of organisms evolved over time.

8.18 Geographic patterns of species' distributions reflect their evolutionary histories.
TAKE-HOME MESSAGE 8-18: Observing geographic patterns of species' distributions, particularly noting similarities and differences among species living close together but in very different habitats and among species living in similar habitats but

located far from one another, helps us to understand the evolutionary histories of populations.

8.19 Comparative anatomy and embryology reveal common evolutionary origins.
TAKE-HOME MESSAGE 8-19: Similarities in the anatomy of different groups of organisms and in their physical appearance as they proceed through their development can reveal common evolutionary origins.

8.20 Molecular biology reveals that common genetic sequences link all life forms.
TAKE-HOME MESSAGE 8-20: All living organisms share the same genetic code. The degree of similarity in the DNA of different species can reveal how closely related they are and the amount of time that has passed since they last shared a common ancestor.

8.21 Laboratory and field experiments enable us to watch evolution in progress.
TAKE-HOME MESSAGE 8-21: Multiply replicated, controlled laboratory selection experiments and long-term field studies of natural populations—including observations on antibiotic-resistant strains of disease-causing bacteria—enable us to watch and measure evolution as it occurs.

Key Terms

adaptation
biogeography
bottleneck effect
convergent evolution
differential reproductive success
directional selection
disruptive selection
evolution
fitness
fixation
fossil
founder effect
gene flow

genetic drift
heritability
homologous structure
inheritance
migration
mutagen
mutation
natural selection
population
radiometric dating
stabilizing selection
trait
vestigial structure

Classroom Catalysts for Chapter 8:
Evolution and Natural Selection

Table of Contents

Activity One: Hammers and Natural Selection

Purpose: Show how allele frequency changes in a population

Time: 15 minutes

Terms: adaptation, allele, fitness, gene, mutation, population

Objective: Introduce students to the concept of allele distribution and how it changes in a population.

Background Information: A key idea for introducing evolution to students is that allele ratios change in a population as their environment changes. Allele ratios for different traits change because the reproductive success of those individuals is better than for others in the population. Should some change in the environment occur, then the allele ratios may change again. This introductory activity uses hammers because most everyone has used at least one during their lives and there are many different kinds of hammers with just two basic parts: the head of the hammer and the handle of the hammer. For the purposes of this exercise we will look at a hammer as a living organism and assume the hammer has two genes, one for the handle and the other for the head of hammer. There will be several alleles for the head and handle of the hammer.

Students will be shown the whole population of hammers and then determine which alleles will be most successful for a given scenario. For example, if there were two types of hammer heads, one rubber and the other iron, which would be most successful at hammering metal nails? Most people will say the hammer with the iron head. Keep in mind that the very early hammers had a head made out of stone. Of the population of hammers that exist today, what percent are now made out of stone?

If the environment changes, then the type of hammer that is more fit will change. If a hammer was needed to hit glass without shattering it, a rubber head would probably be more appropriate. Therefore the allele ratios would change so that very few alleles for iron heads would be in the population and many alleles for rubber heads would be in the population.

Procedure: Have students work in groups of two to three people. The scenario given students is the same as was discussed above, but can be easily modified using other tools. They should discuss which material, rubber or iron, on the head of the hammer would be more successful for hammering metal nails. This is analogous to reproductive success of the hammers. Because most will pick the iron head, then in the future a person would buy more hammers with iron heads and the ratio would not be 50% iron and 50% rubber heads, but may be 90% iron and only 10% rubber. Explain that should an allele for a trait give some advantage that increases reproductive success, then that allele will be more common after many generations in that population.

STUDENT HANDOUT: Hammers and Natural Selection

Purpose: Determine the hammer allele with the best fit for the environment.

Instruction: Hammers are made up of two parts: 1) The handle that you grasp while using, and 2) the head, which is the part you strike against objects. For our purposes you will view the hammer head as one trait with two potential alleles. You are handed a population of hammers. Half of them have rubber heads (one allele) and the other half have iron heads (second allele). You are to determine which type of hammer is best for a given environment.

1. What do you think is meant by a population of hammers?

Part One

1. Choose the hammer head that is best for striking metal nails into wood boards. Explain why you made this choice.

2. If these hammers were living creatures capable of breeding, and needed to strike metal nails to survive, do you think more of them would have iron heads than rubber heads after many generations? Explain your answer.

3. What percentage of the hammers do you think (estimate) would have an allele for iron heads? For rubber heads? Explain your answer.

Part Two

1. This time you introduce your population of hammers into an environment where they must strike glass, without breaking it, to survive. How do you think the allele distribution would change in this case?

2. What do you think would happen to the allele kind and distribution if a mutation occurred producing a hammer head made out of cork?

INSTRUCTOR ANSWER SHEET: Hammers and Natural Selection

Purpose: Determine the hammer allele with the best fit for the environment.

Instruction: Hammers are made up of two parts: 1) The handle that you grasp while using, and 2) the head, which is the part you strike against objects. For our purposes you will view the hammer head as one trait with two potential alleles. You are handed a population of hammers. Half of them have glass heads (one allele) and the other half have iron heads (second allele). You are to determine which type of hammer is best for a given environment.

1. What do you think is meant by a population of hammers?

   Answer: The population of hammers would be all of the individual hammers in a particular environment.

Part One

1. Choose the hammer head that is best for striking metal nails into wood boards. Explain why you made this choice.

   Answer: The iron head would be best. Accept logical answers.

2. If these hammers were living creatures capable of breeding, and needed to strike metal nails to survive do you think more of them would have iron heads than rubber heads after many generations? Explain your answer.

   Answer: More hammers with iron heads will breed because rubber-headed hammers will not be as effective. We could assume rubber-headed hammers will be less healthy and not breed to the same degree as iron hammers.

3. What percentage of the hammers do you think (estimate) would have an allele for iron heads? For rubber heads? Explain your answer.

   Answer: A much higher percentage of iron-headed hammers will make up the population in this environment. The percentage for an allele for a particular trait will directly relate to its ability to improve reproductive success.

Part Two

1. This time you introduce your population of hammers into an environment where they must strike glass, without breaking it, to survive. How do you think the allele distribution would change in this case?

   Answer: The allele distribution may change if the environment changes. What works in one place may not work in another.

2. What do you think would happen to the allele kind and distribution if a mutation occurred producing a hammer head made out of cork?

   Answer: Another allele for hammer heads would be added to the genome and the percentages will change because a new allele is represented in the population.

Activity Two: Natural Selection in Action
(Out-of-class activity)

Purpose: To explore natural selection in a small sample population of animals introduced to an island

Time: 60–90 minutes

Terms: adaptation, allele, fitness, founder effect, gene, genetic drift, population

Objective: Students will explore how environmental factors influence allele selection resulting from the founder effect, a form of genetic drift.

Background Information: During this activity students will confront a scenario in which a small group of horse-like animals are intentionally removed from their main population and transferred to an island that has a slightly different environment. This small random sample of the population has less genetic diversity then the population of origin. This is an example of genetic drift, specifically, the founder effect, which will have an influence on the allele selection that can occur as this new population changes in this slightly different environment.

There are less alleles to choose from than the population of origin. For simplicity sake, there are only two alleles for each trait, although this would probably not be the case in a real population and we assume no mutations occur. Since there are only two alleles for each trait, students will have to choose which allele they think gives individuals in this population a reproductive advantage. Others alleles will give no advantage; students will have to distinguish these.

For example, animals will be faced with a new food source that turns bright red in color when ripened and that is higher up in trees than their previous food source. Animals with long necks and color vision will probably have an advantage, reaching more food and being healthier than their short-necked, colorblind peers.

The temperature on this island is slightly colder than that of the land of origin; therefore, longer fur may give the animals an advantage. There are no natural enemies on the island; therefore, alleles for traits that are for self-defense will not provide a reproductive advantage.

STUDENT HANDOUT: Natural Selection in Action

Table One: A small population of horse-like animals have been removed from a large population of the same creatures and moved to a small island many miles away. The environment of this island is slightly different then the mainland: temperatures are cooler, and the only food source is a fruit that turns bright red when ripe and is located higher up in the trees. The island is only a few square kilometers, and there are no natural enemies.

After many generations you return back to the island and examine that the animal has physically changed as a result of being moved to a new environment. Examine each of the possible alleles for the traits below. Choose an allele for each trait that you believe the animals will possess and explain why you chose that answer.

Allele one	Allele two	Justification
Long hair	Short hair	
Blue eyes	Brown eyes	
Long tail	Short tail	
Long neck	Short neck	
Good hearing	Poor hearing	
Fast runner	Slow runner	
Color vision	No color vision	
Long nose	Short nose	
Long tongue	Short tongue	

On a separate sheet of paper provided draw a picture of the animal, with the alleles chosen in Table One. Also write a description of the animal.

Questions

1. Which of the traits provided no particular advantage to the animal in reproducing? How could you determine this?

2. Why would it be correct to state that this small group of animals reaching and then inhabiting the island was an example of the founder effect, a form of genetic drift?

3. Do you think the future animal will look the same as the population on the mainland from which the animals originated? Explain your answer.

4. What environmental factors do you believe influenced the changes in allele selection?

5. What are adaptations? What adaptations do you think will occur to the animals on the island?

6. Why is it true that the animals found on the island after many generations have greater "fitness" than the animals first introduced to the island?

7. Suppose the water table around the island dropped and the island and mainland were once again joined. What effect would the migration of these animals back to the main population be on the allele frequencies?

INSTRUCTOR ANSWER SHEET: Natural Selection in Action

A small population of horse-like animals have been removed from a large population of the same creatures and moved to a small island many miles away. The environment of this island is slightly different than the mainland: temperatures are cooler, and the only food source is a fruit that turns bright red when ripe and is located higher up in the trees. The island is only a few square kilometers, and there are no natural enemies.

After many generations you return back to the island and examine that the animal has physically changed as a result of being moved to a new environment. Examine each of the possible alleles for the traits below. Choose an allele for each trait that you believe the animals will posses and explain why you chose that answer.

Allele one	Allele two	Justification
Long hair **X**	Short hair	Cooler climate
Blue eye	Brown eyes	Neither has an advantage
Long tail	Short tail	Neither has an advantage
Long neck **X**	Short neck	Reach fruit high up in trees
Good hearing	Poor hearing	Neither gives an advantage
Fast runner	Slow runner	No enemies, neither gives an advantage
Color vision **X**	No color vision	Color vision will allow animals to spot ripened fruit
Long nose	Short nose	Neither gives advantage
Long tongue **X**	Short tongue	Long tongue probably useful for grabbing food

On a separate sheet of paper provided draw a picture of the animal, with the alleles chosen in Table One. Also write a description of the animal.

Questions

1. Which of the traits provided no particular advantage to the animal in reproducing? How could you determine this?
   Answer: Speed, eye color, hearing, tail.

2. Why would it be correct to state that this small group of animals reaching and then inhabiting the island was an example of the founder effect, a form of genetic drift?
   Answer: The allele distribution of the group members is different than the main population from which they came.

3. Do you think the future animal will look the same as the population on the mainland from which the animals originated? Explain your answer.
   Answer: No, traits that allow them to survive and breed in this new environment will become more common.

4. What environmental factors do you believe influenced the changes in allele selection?
   Answer: The food source will be very important. Temperature change will also be a factor.

5. What are adaptations? What adaptations do you think will occur to the animals on the island?
   Answer: An adaptation would be a change in allele frequency in a population which occurs because more individuals in the population with particular alleles breed more successfully then others without these alleles. Long neck and color vision will more likely occur in the population of this island.

6. Why is it true that the animals found on the island after many generations have greater "fitness" than the animals first introduced to the island?
   Answer: The alleles present in the population will more commonly allow individuals to breed because they are better adapted to the environment.

7. Suppose the water table around the island dropped and the island and mainland were once again joined. What effect would the migration of these animals back to the main population be on the allele frequencies?
   Answer: These animals will introduce chromosomes with different proportions of alleles than those present in the main population.

Activity Three: Genetic Drift

Purpose: To illustrate genetic drift

Time: 30 minutes

Terms: genetic drift, allele, population

Objectives: Explore what role change plays in allele frequency

Instructions: Ask the students what happened to a woman's last name when she married in the days before hyphens. [It changed to the husband's.] What happened if a man only had daughters? [His last name disappeared.] This is purely chance. Each time a man has a child he rolls the dice to see if he has a boy or a girl. Each time it is a 50:50 chance. Sometimes a man will roll only daughters, sometimes he will roll only sons, and most times a man will get both sons and daughters, especially if he plays the game long enough. But sometimes a man only has daughters and his last name (and Y-chromosome) is lost from the population. The same thing is true of alleles of genes. Each person has two alleles of each gene (one from mom and one from dad). Each person will pass only half of their genetic material when procreating. It is entirely random which allele is passed to the offspring; sometimes only the paternal allele will be passed to the offspring and the maternal allele gets lost to the population, or the maternal allele is only passed and the paternal one is lost. There is no external event altering the frequency of any allele in the population, just random chance. Over time the allele frequency of a gene will change without any selection event. Genes will "drift" out of the population.

Give each of the students in the front row three black and three red playing cards and ask each student to randomly pick one. Count the red and black cards that appear. Place the cards back in each deck and shuffle them. Draw again and repeat this three times. Count the frequency of black versus red cards. Ask the students to pass the cards to a student behind them and repeat the experiment again. Continue to the third row, and then the fourth. At the end, compare the frequencies of black versus red cards. Sometimes the frequency of black is much higher than red, sometimes the frequency is about equal, and sometimes the red is much more frequent than the black. (Don't repeat much more than three times for each or the numbers will start to approach 50:50 every time.)

At the end you may have a chart like below:

Row	Red vs. Black
1	55:45
2	66:34
3	45:55
4	50:50

Now give each student in row 2 four red cards and two black cards. Repeat the trial. The students should notice by now that black cards are very rare. It should become obvious that if things keep going like this there will be no black cards drawn and eventually only red cards are in the population. Red and black cards are like alleles, you have a 50% chance of drawing either at the beginning. Over time an allele may be lost like the black cards were lost.

Genetic drift reduces diversity in a population.

Activity Four: Mutation

Purpose: To show how genetic mutations permeate a population

Time: 15–30 minutes

Terms: mutation, genetic diversity, generations

Objectives: Explore how mutations occur in populations increasing genetic diversity

Play the old game of telephone. Give each student on the left side of each row a note that reads "I do not like them Sam-I-am, I do not like green hags and yams" (or some other phrase you choose). Do not pick a famous line without altering it a little like above; well-known sayings will be corrected even if only a little of the line is actually heard. Now play telephone. Each person whispers the line into the ear of the person to their right—only once. Then the second person whispers it to the person to their right with the same rules, etc. until it reaches the other end of the row. Ask the last person in each row to write down what they heard. When you started, each message was exactly the same. Some rows will pass the message intact; some will alter the message. The changes in the message are mutations. On the left side of the class there is no genetic diversity. After several generations (each whispered pass) the right side of the room has some (possibly substantial) genetic diversity.

Mutation increases diversity in a population.

Activity Five: If a person does not reproduce or chooses not to, does that make him or her unfit? (p. 21)

Purpose: Define fitness

Time: This discussion could take up to 30–45 minutes, plus about another 20–30 minutes for any online investigation. Total time, if done completely in class = 60–85 minutes.

Terms: fitness, reproduction

Objectives: Discover the implications of not reproducing from an evolutionary standpoint.

In order to answer this question, the students first should be asked to formulate a definition of the term "fitness." This could be done as a general discussion with the entire class or have the class break up into groups, define the term, and then present and justify their definition to the class.

This can also lead to a discussion of the question, "What is the goal of life?" and how a lack of reproduction affects that question. The instructor can then lead the students in a discussion of "fitness" as a term applied to an individual rather than to a population or species. Other questions that could further these lines of discussion are:

1. Does fitness have more to do with choosing to reproduce or being prevented by the environment from reproducing?
2. In order for a species to be considered "fit," should reproduction take place as much as possible?
3. What factors might constrain reproduction within a species?
4. What factors might constrain reproduction within the human species?
5. Can you make the argument that by choosing not to reproduce you might help to make your species more fit?
6. Are there any animal species where some of the individuals choose not to breed?
7. If so, what good are they anyway?
8. Is there any way you can determine if one person is more fit than another?
9. If you think you can determine fitness in another human, do you think you have the right or responsibility to prevent that person from reproducing?
10. What does all this have to do with evolution?
11. How is fitness ultimately decided?
12. Is fitness a matter of foresight or hindsight?

Some of these questions could also be investigated by the students online. For example, questions 6 and 7 very easily lend themselves to an Internet search. Alternatively to running this activity as a discussion, the instructor could present these questions to the students so that they could answer some or all of them in the form of an essay or paper.

The instructor can either present these questions, along with any others that seem pertinent, as they come up in discussion or could present them to the students all at the same time in the form of a worksheet. If the latter choice is made, it should only take a few minutes to type up the questions and run them off for the class. The instructor might also want to set the stage for this discussion by reviewing the historical references to fitness and evolution, which should take about 10 minutes, and then asking for the students' definitions.

Activity Six: Could we ever clone the "perfect" human being?
(p. 23)

Purpose: To explore the consequences of genetic manipulation in human beings for the purpose of perfecting human beings

Time: 30–45 minutes.

Terms: eugenics, "perfect human," cloning

Objectives: Students should develop an informed opinion about the pursuit of perfecting human beings.

Before opening this question up for class discussion, the instructor might want to review the process of cloning, how it works, how often it works, and what it can and cannot accomplish. In order for the students to answer this question, we need to define the key term "perfect." Do we mean perfect physically, mentally, emotionally, socially, morally or some master combination of all of these? We would also have to make the assumption that, at any given time, the "perfect" human being already exists, since cloning requires the use of DNA from an existing organism.

 This can be run as a whole-class discussion. The instructor may ask the students to list the traits that they feel would be important in the "perfect" human and write them on the board. Inevitably this will lead to disagreements as to what traits are positive, neutral, and negative. The class also should be given the opportunity to mention any person (or persons) alive today that comes closest for them to the perfect person, since we do need that existing person for a clone.

 This should also lead to a discussion of the major question, "Who should decide what perfect means?" Should the decision be left up to an individual, a group, the government, scientists, religious leaders, etc.?

 Finally, to put this question into historical perspective, the instructor might want to explain a little about eugenics—when and where it occurred, what it was used for and who were its proponents. After this historical information has been given (or the instructor can have the students research eugenics online), the students can be asked the question again to see if their ideas have changed.

A good overview can be found at http://en.wikipedia.org/wiki/Eugenics. Otherwise, no other out-of-class preparation should be necessary.

Activity Seven: Do we have any other vestigial structures besides the appendix? What possible functions did they have? (p. 33)

Purpose: To explore the presence of vestigial organs in populations

Time: 30–60 minutes

Terms: vestigial organs, evolution

Objectives: Identify what vestigial organs exist in humans and what role they may have played in our evolutionary past.

If laptop or desktop computers with Internet connection are available, this would make a good Web research exercise. If not, the students can be asked to look this up online ahead of time and bring their answers in to class.

It should be interesting to see how many the students come up with, what their sources are and what uses the vestigial structures are thought to have had earlier in our evolution. Some of the possible vestigial structures they could find include:

wisdom teeth   body hair   ability to wiggle the ears   coccyx   goose pimples

This can also lead to a discussion of the following questions:

1. Why have these structures persisted if they no longer have any purpose?
2. If a structure has some minor function, can it still be considered vestigial?
3. Do we have any vestigial DNA?
4. If so, where did it come from, what did it do, what does it do now, and why haven't we lost it?
5. Do other animals have vestigial structures?
6. What are some examples and what might have been their purpose?
7. The instructor might want to do some research on vestigial structures, in humans and in other animals. Online investigation should take about 30 minutes.

The instructor might want to direct the students to some of the following Web sites:
http://en.wikipedia.org/wiki/Vestigial
http://www.livescience.com/animals/top10_vestigial_organs.html
http://www.talkorigins.org/faqs/comdesc/section2.html#vestiges_criticisms
http://health.howstuffworks.com/vestigial-organ.htm

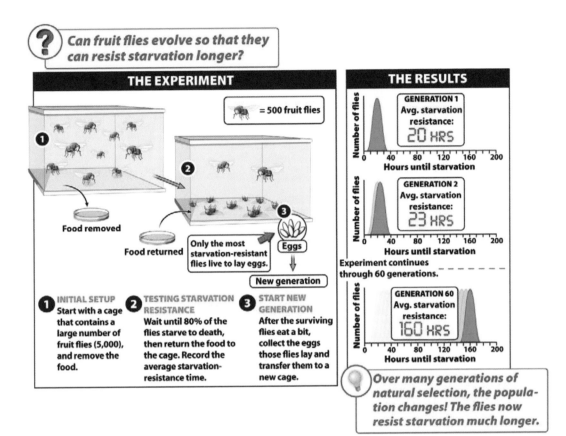

Figure 8-2
What Is Life? A Guide to Biology
© 2010 W. H. Freeman and Company

Figure 8.02 Evolution in action: increasing fruit fly resistance to starvation.

Estimate how many flies of GENERATION 1 above were still alive 20 hours into the experiment. _____

Estimate how long it took until 80% of the flies had starved to death. _____

Estimate how many flies of GENERATION 1 produced eggs for GENERATION 2.

_____

Notice that "time" appears on both sides of Figure. 8.02. On the results side time is given in hours. **Identify** the units of time you'd expect to see on the left if they had been specified. _____

Predict how the outcome of the experiment would have been different, if
a) one waited until 95% of the flies had starved to death in each generation:

b) one waited until 65% of the flies had starved to death in each generation:

TEXTBOOK CONVERSION TOOLS

We offer innovative tools to ease the transition from your current book to *What Is Life? A Guide to Biology*

▶ **CORRELATION GRIDS** align *What Is Life?* coverage with that of the current leading texts in Non-Majors Biology, including chapter-by-chapter and section-by-section breakdowns of topics

▶ **NEW FIGURE CONVERSION ENGINE** allows instructors to correlate figures from their current textbook to figures in *What Is Life?* and easily download the *What Is Life?* figure

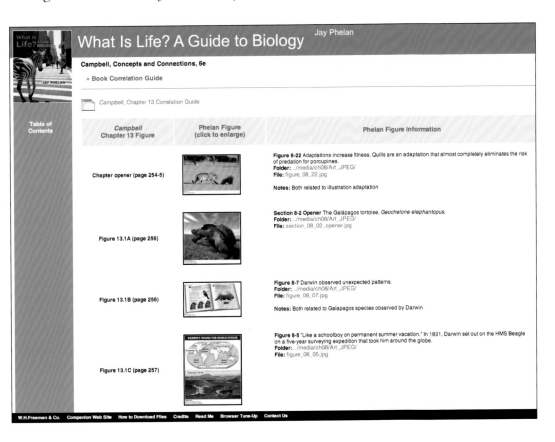

STUDENT RESOURCES—ON THE COMPANION SITE & THE EBOOK

Students who buy new copies of *What Is Life?* are given full access to **PREP-U**, the innovative online quizzing tool created by Jay Phelan that helps students learn Biology. In addition, students in courses using *What Is Life?* will benefit from a variety of study tools found on the **BOOK COMPANION SITE** (www.whfreeman.com/phelan).

Q ANIMATIONS

Student can review the engaging **Q ANIMATIONS** shown by their instructors during lecture to reinforce lessons about hard-to-visualize biological concepts. On the **BOOK COMPANION SITE** and in the **EBOOK** students can access the same animation features they saw in lecture as well as specific features created to aid them during study time.

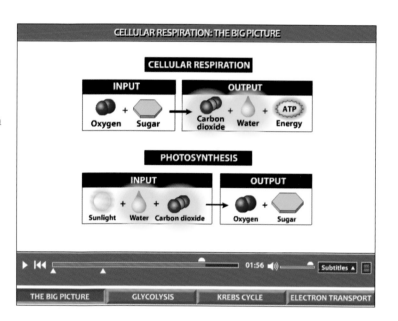

- ▶ Each animation offers **CHECK YOUR UNDERSTANDING** multiple-choice quiz questions at strategic points to make sure students are getting the key lessons and not just passively watching the screen
- ▶ Subtitles (in English or Spanish) can be displayed or hidden—as well as printed out for review
- ▶ Controls make it easy to stop, replay, and restart animations and voiceovers as many times as a student needs

TAKE-HOME MESSAGE AUDIO & VIDEO PODCASTS

Podcasts review each section's Take-Home Message and then give a Challenge Question. Many questions require students to think critically about the information in the section. Answers are provided after a pause. Audio-only and video podcasts with images from the text can be heard on or downloaded from the Book Companion Site and the eBook. The eBook offers interactive versions of each Take-Home Message.

LECTURE ART NOTEBOOK

Textbook figures are key to success for visual learners. During note-taking, students spend time redrawing figures from the text and often miss key points made in lecture. The Lecture Art Notebook offers textbook figures in an easy-to-print PDF format so they can come to lectures with the art—precisely as it appears in their book—in hand. There is a Notebook file for each chapter on the **BOOK COMPANION SITE** and the **EBOOK**.

CHAPTER QUIZZES

Each chapter of the Book Companion Site and eBook offers an interactive chapter quiz with feedback. These short quizzes are in addition to the far more expansive quiz offerings available to students using *What Is Life?* on **PREP-U**.

STUDENT SUCCESS GUIDE FOR PHELAN'S
WHAT IS LIFE?

Meredith Somerville Norris, University of North Carolina–Charlotte
Jennifer Warner, University of North Carolina–Charlotte
Based on a model used successfully with over 10,000
students, the **STUDENT SUCCESS GUIDE** focuses on providing
students with the tools they need to succeed. For each
chapter of *What Is Life?* the **STUDENT SUCCESS GUIDE**
offers…

- ▶ Learning objectives for the chapter
- ▶ An engaging lecture outline that organizes the concepts
  and encourages students to add their own notes
- ▶ Key figures from the text integrated into the lecture
  outline to aid visual learners by associating images
  with concepts
- ▶ Short-answer practice questions
- ▶ Selected multiple-choice practice questions
  from Prep-U
- ▶ List of the key terms and
  their definitions

> **❝❝I loved this study guide and the associated questions. Bravo.❞❞**
> —Alicia Steinhardt, Instructor
> Hartnell Community College

> **❝❝I liked how students could review their concepts with relevant diagrams and charts.❞❞**
> —Lawrence Roberge, Instructor
> Florida Community College, Jacksonville

> **❝❝The Success Guide helped me so much…. The graphs and diagrams made learning easier. I would use this type of study guide for the whole class semester.❞❞**
> — Rachel LaForge, Student
> St. Clair Community College

QUESTIONS ABOUT LIFE READER

Heather Vance-Chalcraft, East Carolina University
Because life is about asking questions!

- ▶ A supplemental booklet that offers biological questions & answers
  from the *Scientific American* feature "Ask the Experts"
- ▶ Practicing biologists answer questions relating to health, wellness,
  and the biological world around us
- ▶ Includes assessment questions for students relating to the feature
  and designed to encourage science writing

When you lose weight, where does it go?

How long can a person survive without food?

How much of human height is genetic and how much is due to nutrition?

What causes a fever?

How do volcanoes affect world climate?

Chapter 8
EVOLUTION AND NATURAL SELECTION

Learning Objectives

- Understand how evolution can be observed in various populations
- Describe Charles Darwin's impact on evolution and the study of biology
- Identify the individuals who influenced Darwin
- Describe Darwin's most important observations
- Explain the four ways evolutionary change can take place
- Identify the difference between evolution and natural selection
- Understand and explain the five different lines of evidence for the occurrence of evolution
- Describe ways evolution can be observed today

Chapter Outline

I. Evolution is an Ongoing Process

- Evolution can be observed by several trials of an experiment with a population of fruit flies.

    o Define the term population.

    o Outline the basic steps of the experiment to increase starvation resistance in fruit flies.

- Define **evolution** in respect to the end result of the fruit fly experiment described in the chapter.

- The findings of the experiment are a result of **natural selection**. This means the flies in subsequent generations were born with traits or characteristics that allowed them to _____ and _____ better than other flies in the population.

II. Darwin Journeyed to a New Idea

- While Charles Darwin is the scientist most commonly associated with the study of evolution, several other scientists influenced Darwin and helped lay the groundwork for his ideas.

  - **Curvier** discovered giant fossils that showed no resemblance to living animals. The only explanation for these fossils was:

  - **Lamarck's** studies suggested:

  - **Lyell**, a geologist, presented the idea:

- Charles Darwin's start in the field:

  - Darwin ended up on the HMS Beagle because:

  - Two of Darwin's most important observations include

    1.

    2.

  - Why did these observations contradict the current scientific thinking of the time?

- Darwin finally published the book entitled _____
  with all of his ideas and observations.

    o Even though Darwin is the sole author of this text, why are both Alfred
       Russel Wallace and Darwin credited for first describing evolution by
       natural selection?

III. Four Mechanisms can Give Rise to Evolution

- Define evolution.

    o The key term *population* should be in the definition above. Scientists
       can genetically modify mice and an individual can change their
       physical features, but *individuals* do not evolve.

- Keeping in mind that the allele frequency in a population can change, list the four
  ways evolutionary change can occur.

    1.

    2.

    3.

    4. Natural Selection

    Natural Selection is not the same as evolution. It is one of the following four
    agents of change.

A. Mutations

- A mutation is:

- Mutations can be caused by several very different factors. Two nonspecific, common causes involve:

  1.

  2.

  a. _____ are chemicals or agents in the environment that increase the rate of mutation.

  b. List two examples of potential sources of radiation that may cause mutations.

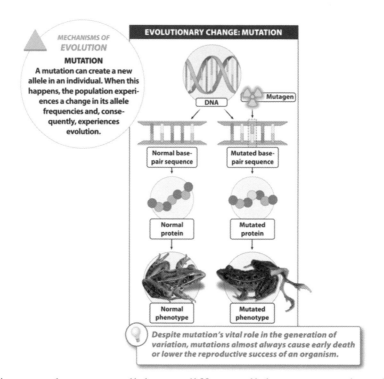

- A mutation can change one allele to a different allele or create a brand new allele. Describe how this can then affect the resulting protein product.

B. Genetic Drift

- Genetic drift can be defined as:

- Is the impact of genetic drift seen more greatly in large populations or small populations?

- Genetic drift can occur to the extent where the frequency of an allele in a population is 100%; actually reducing the genetic diversity within the population. This consequence is referred to as _____.

- Genetic drift is different from natural selection because its impact is not directly linked to reproductive success. Give your own example of a trait that might be impacted by genetic drift.

- Two specific impacts of genetic drift are:

  1. Founder effect

     o Explain the end result of this effect.

  2. Population bottlenecks

     o Describe what happens in a population bottleneck.

        - These events are due to:

        - How do these events affect evolution?

C. Migration

- Migration is also called _____, which is:

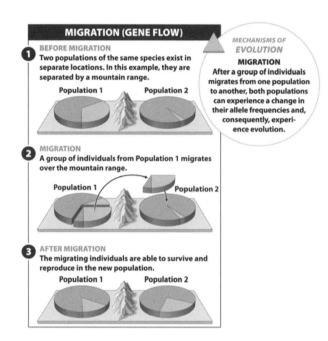

- Can both populations involved in migration experience an impact? Explain.

D. Natural Selection

- This chapter introduces us to evolution through natural selection with the fruit fly starvation resistance experiment. Darwin outlined this agent of change in his famous text. In your own words, define natural selection.

- There are three specific conditions that need to be present in order for natural selection to occur.

    o Condition 1 is _____, which can encompass:

        - physical
        - physiological
        - biochemical
        - behavioral

    Explain what is needed to satisfy this first condition.

    o Condition 2 is _____.

    o Condition 3 is _____. In your own words, summarize this condition:

IV. Through Natural Selection, Populations of Organisms can become Adapted to their Environment.

A. There are many misconceptions surrounding the phrase "survival of the fittest," including the fact that Darwin did not first utilize this phrase!

Since **fitness** greatly impacts natural selection and evolution, and it doesn't refer to how fast someone can run the mile, define fitness in respect to natural selection.

In two sentences or less, define the three aspects important to the (evolutionary) fitness of an individual.

1.

2.

3.

B. Adaptation

Adaptation refers to

_____ *and*

_____.

C. Artificial Selection

The three conditions necessary for natural selection are also satisfied in artificial selection, but the difference is that reproductive success is determined by _____ rather than nature.

Explain a situation where a breeder or farmer would benefit from utilizing natural selection.

D. Natural Selection

1. Natural selection can lead to change, but not "perfection."

   In you own words, briefly explain the factors that support this statement: "A population will never be, what some might consider, perfect."

2. Natural selection can select for change in simple traits.

    Many populations have a range of traits that can be greatly influenced by natural selection. The variation of traits results in a variation of phenotypes. Complete the following chart to highlight the influence of natural selection.

    Changes can occur in three major ways:

Type of Selection	What occurs?	Example

3. Natural selection can select for change in complex traits.

    Some traits that are more complex, such as certain behaviors, may also be affected by natural selection. The three conditions necessary for natural selection to occur are still satisfied, even though some of the traits involve multiple physiological systems.

    Give an example of how natural selection could affect a specific behavior.

V. The Evidence for the Occurrence of Evolution is Overwhelming

The following five unique areas of evidence help us better understand Darwin's original thoughts and have advanced all areas of biology.

A. Fossil Record

- While fossils are often though of as "old bones," technically, fossils are:

- Briefly explain how radioactive isotopes are utilized in fossil records.

- List three ways the analysis of fossil records helps to provide evidence for the process of natural selection.

    1.

    2.

    3.

B. Biogeography

- Define biogeography in your own words.

- What is unique about the biogeographic pattern of some of the organisms in Australia?

C. Embryology and Anatomy

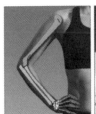    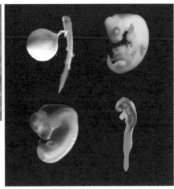

- By examining the vertebrate embryo and various aspects of anatomy, one can identify common features, or _____.

- Briefly explain what a vestigial structure is and list a common example.

D. Our DNA

- New technology has allowed us to sequence, or map out, our genetic code (DNA). This has also been successful in many other species.

- Patterns can be noted in examining the DNA sequence of various organisms. If you were examining the DNA of a brother and sister, would the sequences look more or less similar than the DNA of the brother as compared to his cousin?

    o   Why?

- To compare DNA sequences between species, an individual gene that produces a specific protein can be examined. Proteins are made up of building blocks called amino acids. Therefore, comparing the amino acids will help compare the DNA sequences.

- In examining the beta chain of the hemoglobin protein, it has been found that humans have _____ (number of) amino acids in the beta chain.

- In comparison:

    o Rhesus monkeys have _____ (number of) amino acids that are *different* as compared to the human sequence.
    o Dogs have _____ amino acids that are different.
    o Birds have _____ amino acids that are different.
    o Lamprey eels have _____ amino acids that are different.

- Explain what this means:

E. Using the Scientific Method to see Evolution in Action

- Just as the fruit fly starvation resistance experiment illustrated in the first section of the chapter, carefully planned and executed experiments both in the lab and in the field allow us to observe and learn about evolution as it occurs.

- The evolution of bacteria has led to a very important public health concern of today.

    o Define an "antibiotic-resistant strain of bacteria."

    o How have bacteria become resistant to pharmaceuticals such as penicillin?

Testing and Applying Your Understanding

Multiple Choice

1. Evolution is defined as:
   a) a change in the frequency of alleles in a population over time.
   b) a change in the frequency of a morphological trait in a population over time.
   c) a progressive "ladder" of changes from most primitive organisms to most advanced organisms.
   d) a change in a morphological trait of an individual during its lifetime.
   e) survival of the fittest.

2. Which of the following statements about Charles Darwin is FALSE?
   a) He dropped out of medical school.
   b) He and Alfred Russel Wallace independently came up with the theory of evolution by natural selection.
   c) He married his first cousin.
   d) He spent five years traveling the world observing living organisms and collecting fossils
   e) He influenced Malthus's ideas about the limits of population growth.

3. The average time to death from starvation in a fruit fly is about 20 hours. Selecting for increased starvation resistance in fruit flies:
   a) can produce populations in which the average time to death from starvation is 10 hours.
   b) has no effect because it is not a trait that influences fruit fly fitness.
   c) has no effect because it is too complex a physiological process, dependent upon the effects of too many genes.
   d) can produce populations in which the average time to death from starvation is more than 160 hours.
   e) has little effect because constant mutation reduces starvation resistance, counteracting any benefits from selection.

4. To demonstrate evolution by natural selection, all of the following conditions must be satisfied EXCEPT:
   a) variation for a trait.
   b) heritability of a trait.
   c) differential reproductive success.
   d) genetic drift.
   e) All of the above are necessary for evolution by natural selection.

5. Evolution occurs:
   a) only through natural selection.
   b) only when the environment is changing.
   c) only via natural selection, genetic drift, migration, or mutation.
   d) almost entirely because of directional selection.
   e) by altering physical traits but not behavioral traits.

6. _____ selection favors organisms that have character values at both extremes of the phenotypic distribution.
   a) Disruptive
   b) Stabilizing
   c) Directional
   d) Intense
   e) Intermittent

7. Which of the following statements is NOT consistent with evolution by natural selection?
   a) Individuals in a population exhibit variation, some of which can be inherited by their offspring.
   b) Individuals change during their lifespans to fit their environment better, and these changes can be inherited by their offspring.
   c) Natural selection can lead to speciation.
   d) Individuals that reproduce most successfully are more likely to have offspring that also reproduce successfully if the environment remains stable.
   e) Certain individuals in a population have a higher rate of reproductive success than other individuals due to a variety of environmental and developmental factors.

8. All of the following statements are true about mutations EXCEPT:
   a) The origin of genetic variation is mutation.
   b) A mutation is any change in an organism's DNA.
   c) Mutations are almost always random with respect to the needs of the organism.
   d) Most mutations are beneficial or neutral to the organism in which they occur.
   e) The mutation rate can be affected by exposure to radiation.

9. "Survival of the fittest" may be a misleading phrase to describe the process of evolution by natural selection because:
   a) survival matters less to natural selection than reproductive success does.
   b) it is impossible to determine the fittest individuals in nature.
   c) natural variation in a population is generally too great to be influenced by differential survival.
   d) reproductive success on its own does not necessarily guarantee evolution.
   e) fitness has little to do with natural selection.

10. A population is:
   a) a group of species that share the same habitat.
   b) a group of individuals of the same species that have the potential to interbreed.
   c) a group of individuals of the same species that live in the same general location and have the potential to interbreed.
   d) a group of individuals of related species that live in the same general location and have the potential to interbreed.
   e) a group of individuals of the same species that live in the same general location and have the same genotypes.

11. Birth weight in human babies is generally:
    a) subject to stabilizing selection.
    b) not a heritable trait.
    c) a strong predictor of adult weight.
    d) subject to disruptive selection.
    e) All of the above.

12. Artificial selection was used on corn to produce a single strain of corn with increased growth rates and greater resistance to a fungus. Although farmers have continued to select for these traits, however, the productivity of this strain is no longer increasing. This suggests that:
    a) the population size has been decreasing.
    b) artificial selection is not as strong as natural selection.
    c) gene migration is a major evolutionary agent in corn.
    d) all or most of the natural variation for these traits has been eliminated.
    e) long-term disruptive selection may lead to speciation.

13. In a fish population in a shallow stream, the genotypic frequency of yellowish-brown fish and greenish-brown fish changed significantly after a flash-flood randomly swept away individuals from that stream. This change in genotypic frequency is most likely attributable to:
    a) gene flow.
    b) disruptive selection.
    c) directional selection.
    d) genetic drift.
    e) the founder effect.

14. Which of the following best explains why genetic bottlenecks and founder effects are evolutionarily important?
    a) In both cases, strong selective pressures lead to fast directional selection.
    b) Both result in stabilizing selection due to strong selective pressures.
    c) Both result in small populations subject to genetic drift.
    d) Both result in increased fitness.
    e) Both a) and d) are correct.

15. The phenotypic trait of polydactyly, where an individual has extra fingers or toes, is one symptom of Ellis-van Creveld syndrome. This syndrome is more commonly found in Old Order Amish populations. Which of the following is a possible explanation for why this occurs within this population?
    a) The Old Order Amish experience the "founder effect," where all the members of a population descend from a small group of founding individuals.
    b) The Old Order Amish live near biowaste dumping sites that increase their number of genetic mutations and result in strange disorders.
    c) The Old Order Amish experience the "bottleneck effect" because they are physically isolated from other communities.
    d) Both answers a) and c) are correct.
    e) None of the above is correct.

16. In 1988, a biologist named Richard Lenski introduced 12 genetically identical populations of E. coli to test tubes and subjected them to the same conditions: a period of growth followed by starvation. After several years, all 12 strains had adapted to the conditions in similar ways; however, their genetic sequences were very different. Which of the following conclusions from this experiment is CORRECT?
    a) The 12 E. coli populations underwent convergent evolution resulting from similar environmental conditions.
    b) Similar phenotypes may result from a variety of underlying genotypes.
    c) Evolution by natural selection can be directly observed in organisms with short generation times.
    d) Similar selective pressures on genetically identical organisms can have different effects at the level of the genome.
    e) All of the above are correct conclusions drawn from Richard Lenski's experiments.

17. Which one of the following best describes the difference between artificial and natural selection?
    a) Natural selection acts without the input of humans; artificial selection requires human input.
    b) Natural selection's efficacy is limited by physiological and developmental constraints such as epistasis and pleiotropy; artificial selection's efficacy is free of these constraints.
    c) Natural selection works on all species; artificial selection will only work on lab-reared species.
    d) Charles Darwin understood natural selection but was unaware of artificial selection in his time.
    e) Artificial selection has produced many of the most delicious food items for humans; natural selection has not.

Short Answer

1. Explain the difference between evolution and natural selection.

2. Does evolution occur in individuals or populations? Explain.

3. In describing the results of evolution (e.g. "The finches evolved to have harder beaks"), it often seems as if populations changed with intent or to reach a specific goal. Explain why this does not accurately describe how evolution occurs.

4. What is the difference between natural selection and genetic drift?

5. Why would genetic drift be important to endangered species?

6. Using the fruit fly experiment explained in the text, explain how the three conditions necessary for natural selection were in place.

7. Certain crustaceans have exoskeletons (shells) for protection. Some types of exoskeletons are thinner allowing for the organism to move quickly out of harm's way. However, the thinner exoskeletons are more easily penetrated or punctured by a predator. The evolution of the exoskeletons' thickness in certain populations would reflect what manner of natural selection?

8. Explain how bats that have developed superior echolocation are an illustration of evolutionary adaptation. Be specific.

9. An organism itself isn't necessarily "fit" to survive, but do the alleles "survive" in a population? Explain why or why not.

10. Give an example that demonstrates each of the five lines of evidence for evolution.

11. What is a vestigial structure? Include an example in your explanation.

12. Could the recent development of antibiotic-resistant bacteria be a result of natural selection, artificial selection, or both? Justify your answer.

8 Evolution and Natural Selection

Darwin's dangerous idea

KEY TERMS

Listed in the order of (first text appearance)

- **EVOLUTION**

[Lat., *evolvere,* to roll out]

A change in allele frequencies of a population, which over time produce a population with new or modified characteristics. (p.000)

- **population**

A group of organisms of the same species living in a particular geographic region. (p.000)

- **trait**

A genetically determined characteristic of an organism, such as red eye color or a cleft chin. (p.000)

- **mutation**

[Lat., *mutare,* to change]
An alteration of the base-pair sequence of an individual's DNA. (p.000)

- **mutagen**

[Lat., *mutare,* to change + *genus,* descent or origin]
An agent capable of causing mutation; may be chemical (as some insecticides) or physical (as radiation). (p.000)

- **natural selection**

A mechanism of evolution that occurs when there is heritable variation for a trait and individuals with one version of the trait have greater reproductive success than do individuals with a different version of the trait. (p.000)

- **GENETIC DRIFT**

[Gk. *genos,* race, family]
A random change in allele frequencies over successive generations, a cause of evolution. (p.000)

- **fixation**

The point at which the frequency of an allele in a population is 100% and, therefore, there is no more variation in the population for this gene. Fixation occurs as a consequence of genetic drift. (p.000)

• FOUNDER EFFECT

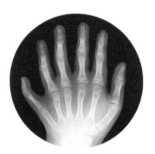

A change in allele frequencies of a population resulting from the isolation of a small subgroup of a larger population; all the descendents of the smaller group will reflect the allele frequencies of the subgroup, which may be different from those of the larger source population. The founder effect is one cause of genetic drift. (p.000)

• bottleneck effect

A change in allele frequencies of a population due to famine, disease, or rapid environmental disturbance that causes a large proportion of the individuals in a population to die. A population bottleneck causes genetic drift. (p.000)

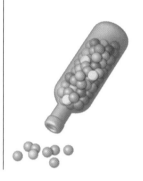

• migration (gene flow)
[Lat., *migrare,* to move from place to place]

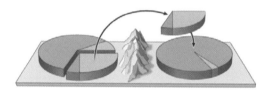

Change in the allele frequencies of a population due to the movement of some individuals of a species from one population to another, changing the allele frequencies of the population they join. (p.000)

• INHERITANCE (HERITABILITY)

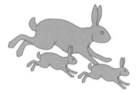

The transmission of traits from parents to their offspring via genetic information. (p.000)

• differential reproductive success

The tendency of some individuals to be more likely than others to survive and reproduce in their environment and thus be able to transmit their genetic traits. Along with variation and heritability, one of the three mandatory conditions necessary for natural selection to occur. (p.000)

• fitness
A measure of the relative reproductive output of an individual with a given phenotype, compared with that of individuals with other phenotypes. (p.000)

adaptation

1 The process by which, as a result of natural selection, organisms become better matched to their environment; *2* a specific feature, such as the quills of a porcupine, that makes an organism more fit. (p.000)

• directional selection

Selection that, for a given trait, increases fitness at one extreme of the phenotype and greatly reduces fitness at the other, leading to the prevalence of one extreme version of the trait in the population. (p.000)

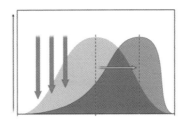

• stabilizing selection

Selection that, for a given trait, produces the greatest fitness at the intermediate point of the phenotypic range. (p.000)

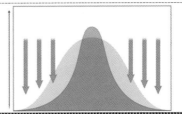

• disruptive selection

Selection that, for a given trait, increases fitness at one extreme of the phenotype and greatly reduces fitness at the intermediate point of the phenotype range; these populations thus have most members at either end of the phenotype range but relatively few in the middle. (p.000)

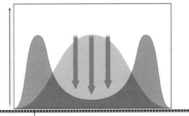

• fossil

[Lat., *fossilis,* that which is dug up]

The remains of a long-past organism, usually its hard parts such as shell, bones, or teeth, which have been naturally preserved; also, traces of such an organism, such as footprints. (p.000)

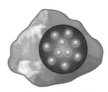

• radiometric dating

A method of determining both the relative and the absolute ages of objects such as fossils by measuring both the radioactive isotopes they contain, which are known to decay at a constant rate, and their decay products. (p.000)

• biogeography

[Gk. *bios,* life + *geo-,* earth + *graphein,* to write down]
The study and interpretation of distribution patterns of living organisms around the world. (p.000)

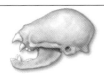

• VESTIGIAL STRUCTURE
[Lat., *vestigium,* footprint or trace]

A structure once useful to an organism but which lost its function as the organism evolved; examples are the human appendix and molars in bats that consume a liquid diet. (p.000)

• homologous structure

[Gk., *homologia,* agreement]
Similarities found in the body structures of organisms that, although modified extensively over time for to serve different functions in different species, are due to inheritance from a common evolutionary ancestor. (p.000)

LAB SOLUTIONS

We offer a variety of options for your Non-Majors Biology laboratory. Whether you want to publish your original experiments in an expertly produced manual, mix existing labs with your own, or adapt a complete manual developed by another college or university, we can provide what you need, completely tailored for your lab course.

FREEMAN BIOLOGY LABPARTNER

Create a custom lab manual from a wide selection of experiments published by W. H. Freeman and Hayden-McNeil Publishing. Choose from a variety of traditional and inquiry-based labs and add content on lab techniques and safety. Reorder the labs to fit your syllabus and include your original experiments. Bind in carbonless graph paper and a pocket folder if you like. Choose from six cover designs and customize for your course; print reference material on the inside cover. The choices are yours, and LabPartner makes it easy! Go to **WWW.WHFREEMAN.COM/LABPARTNER** to learn more. Minimum order: 50 copies.

FREEMAN CUSTOM PUBLISHING

If you prefer to publish only original labs for your course we can publish your work in style, bound in a full-color cover customized to your college or university. All Freeman Custom Publishing authors retain their own copyright. Add graph paper or a pocket folder. Choose from paperback, spiral, or loose-leaf formats. Minimum annual enrollment: 100 copies.

> **We chose W. H. Freeman / Worth Publishers as our custom publisher because they were able to deliver specialized custom content, which was relevant to our course and our students, in a highly professional package at a competitive price.**
>
> —H. M. Pylypiw and T. Luersen
> Quinnipiac University

HAYDEN-MCNEIL

Hayden-McNeil, Freeman's sister company, sets the gold standard in service and quality for qualifying customers, creating dynamic partnerships with educators and producing exceptional course materials at a fair price to students. All Hayden-McNeil authors retain their own copyrights. H-M's exemplary service offerings include:

- ► A dedicated editor devoted to shepherding the production of your lab manual from beginning to end
- ► Professional typesetting and design
- ► Customized scientific illustrations
- ► Access to a searchable online image database
- ► Full-color covers

Minimum annual enrollment: 1000 copies.

In addition to our laboratory manuals, Hayden-McNeil is the leading provider of carbonless student laboratory notebooks used for experimental data reporting and record keeping. To learn more, please talk with your W. H. Freeman representative.

BIOPORTAL/COURSE CARTRIDGES

BIO P⊕RTAL

Designed by instructors and education researchers, **BIOPORTAL** combines a full eBook and the full student media program from the book in one affordable, customizable, and easy-to-use learning space. Whether you need to connect to your campus course management solution, want to use the Portal as a standalone course solution, or just want your students to have access to the eBook and resources, the Portal is the perfect solution to your needs.

All resources are also offered in **BLACKBOARD** and **WEBCT**. Other system course cartridges available upon request.